Bad mood bea
bad day

CROSS HAND
C.? ?AFFIC
SH?? ?? ?E
HAR?? ?? LANE
E ???? ??D
TN?? ??X
?? ?G

Bad mood bear's bad day

John Richardson

Red Fox

For Gaye

A Red Fox Book

Published by Random House Children's Books
20 Vauxhall Bridge Road, London SW1V 2SA

A division of Random House UK Ltd
London Melbourne Sydney Auckland
Johannesburg and agencies throughout the world

© John Richardson 1992

First published by Hutchinson Children's Books 1992
Red Fox edition 1994

1 3 5 7 9 10 8 6 4 2

Printed in China

RANDOM HOUSE UK Limited Reg. No. 954009

ISBN 0 09 915020 4

Bear was lonely. His best friends, the Pig twins and Goat, had gone fishing without him. 'Fed up,' he muttered to himself.

Grandad was busy tending his pumpkins when Bear shuffled by.
  'Hello,' said Bear. 'Want to play?'
  'Oh, hello,' replied Grandad absent-mindedly.
  Bear accidentally stood on one of his seedlings.
  'Do be careful, Bear!' snapped Grandad.

Grandma was busy building a model tower with used matchsticks when Bear sidled into the shed.

'What are you doing, Grandma?' asked Bear, helpfully giving the glue a stir.

'Don't touch!' growled Grandma.

Bear knew when he wasn't wanted and he ambled off to find Mum.

Bear bent down and peered under the car.

  'Hello, Mum!' he beamed. 'Need any help?'

  Mum's oily face peered back at him. 'Rotten clutch,' she snarled. 'Pass me the monkey wrench, dear.'

  Bear passed her a spanner.

  'No!' snapped Mum. 'The monkey wrench! There, no, next to that grommet! Oh, I'll do it myself.'

Bear thought that Dad might feel like a surprise.

'Boo, got you!' he laughed, bashing through Dad's newspaper.
Dad lost his temper.

'Look what you've done!' he cried, picking up the sheets.
'Can't anyone get any peace around here without that little bear
always jumping about?'

Bear began to feel cross too.
  'I only want to play,' he grumbled. 'I'm in a bad mood now!'

Mum was washing her hands when Bear stamped in.
'Grrrrrr,' he growled at her.

Dad was making a cup of tea when Bear growled by.

'Grrrrrrrrrrrrr, grrrrr, grrrrr!' he went.

'Playing tigers!' said Dad, and he laughed out loud. 'That's a good bear.'

Bear didn't like being laughed at when he wasn't trying to be funny.

That night Bear put himself to bed. He was in such a bad mood
that he didn't even want a story. He punched his pillow and
growled himself to sleep.

Bear woke up next morning in a determined mood. 'Things are going to change around here!' he said to himself.

   Dad was making Bear's favourite porridge when Bear hopped into the kitchen.

'Goodness,' said Dad.

'Good heavens!' said Mum.

'Good morning,' said Bear, as if there was nothing unusual about wearing swimming trunks, a snorkel, a bow tie and Wellington boots to breakfast.

'Yuck, porridge!' he said, and he looked at his bowl as if porridge
was his most unfavourite food.

    Mum looked at Dad. 'Something's up,' she said.

Grandad was pruning the roses when Bear roly-polyed past.
  'Goodnight!' yelled Bear, surprising the postman.
  Grandad looked at Bear. 'But it's the *morning*,' he said.

The Pig twins were busy digging a hole to trap Goat in when Bear burst through the hedge.

'You look bonkers,' they chanted.

Bear just stood on his head and whistled.

'He *is* bonkers,' said Goat, coming out from his hiding place in the hedge and falling into the hole.

Grandma watched from the window. 'That little bear's behaving very oddly,' she said to Mum. 'He's talking to the tortoise.'

'Do you think he's all right?' Mum asked worriedly.

'I'd better see to him,' said Dad.

'Oh dear,' said Grandma, 'he's talking to the tree now.'

'And then we can go to the seaside,' said Bear to the tree.

Dad smiled at Bear. 'Can I come too?' he asked.

'If you want to,' sighed Bear and he strolled off to find his bucket and spade.

'Psst, is he all right?' called Mum from behind the shed.

'No, he's gone bonkers,' said the Pig twins.

'He spends too much time on his own,' called Grandad from the cabbages.

Everyone set off to find Bear.
  Bear was digging furiously in the sandpit.

'Hello, can we help?' they said.

Bear was happy playing with everyone, until . . .
. . . Grandad stood on his sandcastle.
   'Be careful!' snapped Bear.

And Grandma began to use the pile of sand Bear needed for his tower.

'Don't touch!' growled Bear.

And when Bear asked Mum to pass him the trowel she passed him the spade instead.

'No, not the *spade*, the *trowel!*' snapped Bear. 'Oh, I'll get it myself.'

Mum tottered off feeling she was just in the way.

'Let's have some fun!' cried Dad, jumping into the pit and making the sand fly.

'Oh, can't I play without that big bear jumping everywhere?' grumbled Bear.

Then the Pig twins took Bear's buckets just when he needed them.

'OH, GO AWAY!' cried Bear, 'or I'll *never* finish this castle.'

Before long, everything was peaceful and quiet. 'Thank goodness,'
said Bear. 'Sometimes it's just nice to be on your own.'

Some
bestselling Red Fox
picture books

THE BIG ALFIE AND ANNIE ROSE STORYBOOK
by Shirley Hughes
OLD BEAR
by Jane Hissey
OI! GET OFF OUR TRAIN
by John Burningham
DON'T DO THAT!
by Tony Ross
NOT NOW, BERNARD
by David McKee
ALL JOIN IN
by Quentin Blake
THE WHALES' SONG
by Gary Blythe and Dyan Sheldon
JESUS' CHRISTMAS PARTY
by Nicholas Allan
THE PATCHWORK CAT
by Nicola Bayley and William Mayne
MATILDA
by Hilaire Belloc and Posy Simmonds
WILLY AND HUGH
by Anthony Browne
THE WINTER HEDGEHOG
by Ann and Reg Cartwright
A DARK, DARK TALE
by Ruth Brown
HARRY, THE DIRTY DOG
by Gene Zion and Margaret Bloy Graham
DR XARGLE'S BOOK OF EARTHLETS
by Jeanne Willis and Tony Ross
WHERE'S THE BABY?
by Pat Hutchins

The story continues at
www.alicesbearshop.com

Alice's Bear Shop is brought to you by Charlie Bears

Illustrations & story copyright © 2018 Rikey Austin
All rights reserved

ISBN 978-1-912878-05-5

Published in 2018 by Charlie Bears Ltd
The Bearhouse, Pipers Close, Pennygillam Industrial Estate,
Launceston, Cornwall, PL15 7PJ, United Kingdom

www.alicesbearshop.com
www.charliebears.com

WOODROFFE
GROWLS AGAIN
Rikey Austin

Alice lived in a run-of-the-mill house with her cat and her dog and her ordinary family. But Alice was not an ordinary little girl because when Alice talked to bears, the bears talked back.

It all began when Jack caught chicken pox. Jack was Alice's big brother, but when he caught chicken pox and became spotty all over he was like a big baby. None of his toys pleased him.

He was bored. Nothing would make him smile.

So Alice's mother went up into the attic to see if there were any
old toys that might amuse Jack. There was an old broken model boat,
a twisted tennis racket and a tatty bear. She left the boat and the racket
and brought down the bear.

She showed Jack how the bear growled
when he was tipped upside down.
Jack smiled. Jack was soon well again,
but he still liked to play with the old bear.

But one day the bear stopped growling. Jack shook him hard but the old bear would not make a sound. Jack sat the bear on the chair next to his bed and soon forgot all about him.

That night, as Alice was making her way up
to bed, she heard a miserable sniffling from Jack's
empty bedroom. She tiptoed inside, following the
sound, and knelt down near to the chair.

"Hello," said Alice. "What's wrong?"
"I...I daren't growl anymore," sniffed the bear.
"My stitching is coming loose and I'm not sure how long
it will last if I keep getting tipped upside down."

Alice thought for a moment. "Do you enjoy growling?" she asked.

"Oh, yes!" said the bear and smiled proudly.
"I've always been a very good growler."
"Could we ask my mum to take a look at your stitching?" asked Alice.
 "She's very good at sewing."

The bear nodded and let Alice pick him up and carry him down the stairs.

Alice's mum was surprised to see Alice out of bed, but when Alice explained she smiled kindly.

"If we fix his stitching he might not mind growling again," said Alice. Her mum took the bear and turned him over gently. "I'm not sure about his growl, Alice, he is an old bear now, but I do see what you mean, he is a little loose in places."

She fetched her sewing box and set to work. "Did you know he used to be my bear, Alice? His name is Woodroffe. My dad bought him for me on my fifth birthday. I was so happy I didn't know who to hug first when he gave him to me!"

Alice lay on the floor at her mother's feet and listened to stories about her mother when she was young and her adventures with Woodroffe.

When her mother was finished
she snipped the last thread
with her sewing scissors and
gingerly turned Woodroffe over.

Grrrrrrrrrrrrrr!

Mum laughed in surprise, but Alice just smiled.

Alice carried the bear upstairs
and placed him back on Jack's bedside chair.
Woodroffe beamed up at Alice.

"Thank you, Miss," he said.
"You can call me Alice," she said and gave him
a kiss on his big, soft, furry cheek.

Jack was pleased when he found the old bear was fixed, but he did feel that he was rather big for teddy bears now, so when Alice finally went to bed that night…

...she found Woodroffe sitting on her pillow.

The next day Alice asked her mum to teach her how to sew.
Her friends began to bring her their most loved-to-bits bears.

S he would listen patiently to each bear's story, and then Alice and her mum would mend them as best they could.

W ord spread quickly and soon Alice and her mum became so busy mending bears they decided to open a bear shop with a special hospital for poorly bears.

Can you guess what they called it?

Alice's Bear Shop
(and hospital for poorly bears)